My Book

_____

_____

Little Girls

Words and Pictures by Stina Nagel

Stardust
Books

THE C. R. GIBSON COMPANY
NORWALK, CONNECTICUT

Copyright MCMLXV by
The C. R. Gibson Company, Norwalk, Connecticut
All rights in this book are reserved.
Printed in United States of America.
Library of Congress Catalog Card Number 65-20122

Little girls are wonderful.

God makes them all . . . yet they

are as different as can be.

Some of them are short,

some of them are tall . . .

and some are in-between.

Many little girls live in big busy cities, while others live in the peaceful country or in friendly little towns.

There are little girls who have brothers and sisters, and there are some who have none.

They all go to school . . .

and they all like to play.

Some play house . . .

others dance . . .

or paint pictures.

Little girls delight in

ice cream, and in parties

and pretty dresses . . .

. . . and in soft snuggly things.

Some like to skip rope and
to swing . . . while others enjoy
reading, gathering flowers,
or make-believe.

And even though all little girls
are different . . . there is one time
when they are all alike.
At the end of each day every little
girl loves to climb on Mommy's or
Daddy's lap, say her prayers,
then snuggle down to sleep in
her cozy bed . . .

JUST LIKE YOU!

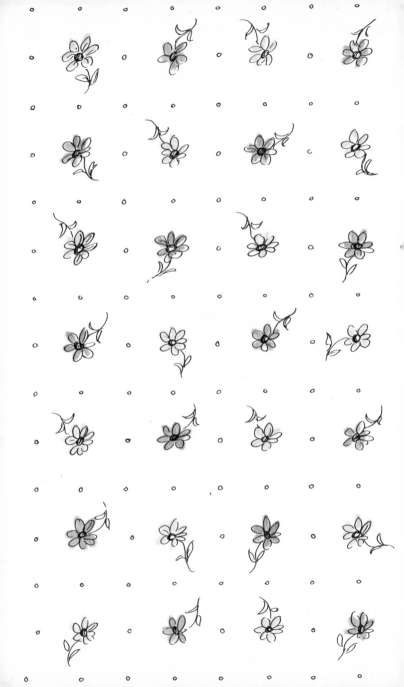